Selections from
innocent eyes
Delta Goodrem

Wise Publications
part of The Music Sales Group

London / New York / Paris / Sydney / Copenhagen / Berlin / Madrid / Tokyo

Published by:
Wise Publications

Exclusive distributors:
Music Sales Limited, Distribution Centre, Newmarket Road,
Bury St Edmunds, Suffolk IP33 3YB, England.
Music Sales Pty Limited
120 Rothschild Avenue, Rosebery, NSW 2018, Australia.

Order No. AM85135
ISBN 0-7119-2691-3
This book © Copyright 2003 by Wise Publications.

Arrangements by Tony Celiberti (Scarlet Music) & Derek Jones.
Design by Glen Hannah.

Printed in the United Kingdom.

www.musicsales.com

Your Guarantee of Quality:

As publishers, we strive to produce every book
to the highest commercial standards.

This book has been carefully designed to minimise
awkward page turns and to make playing from it a real pleasure.

Particular care has been given to specifying
acid-free, neutral-sized paper made from pulps which
have not been elemental chlorine bleached.

This pulp is from farmed sustainable forests and
was produced with special regard for the environment.

Throughout, the printing and binding have been
planned to ensure a sturdy, attractive publication
which should give years of enjoyment.

If your copy fails to meet our high standards,
please inform us and we will gladly replace it.

Innocent Eyes

Words & Music by Delta Goodrem & Vince Pizzinga

7

In My Own Time

Words & Music by Delta Goodrem

spinn - ing a - round___ and it's mak - ing me___ di - zzy.___ I'm spinn - ing a - round___ ___ and it's mak - ing me___ ill.___ You don't un - der - stand___ what I'm go - ing through just to, find a way___ to___ climb.___ 'Cause it - 'll be___

Chorus

___ in my own___ time.___

In my own time.

Not Me, Not I

Words & Music by Delta Goodrem, Eliot Kennedy, Gary Barlow & Kara Dioguardi

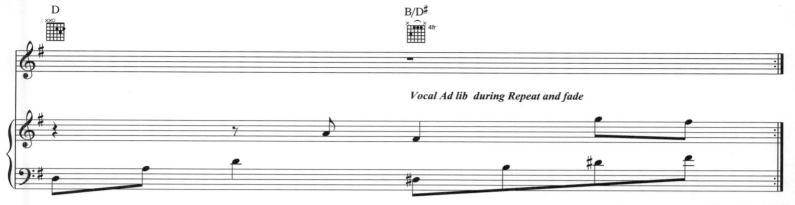

Vocal Ad lib during Repeat and fade

Repeat and fade

(Additional lyrics)

Verse 2

The story goes on without you.
There's got to be another ending.
Yeah, you broke my heart, it won't be the last time.
But I"ll get over them too.
As a new door opens we close the ones behind,
And if you search your soul I know you'll find,
You never really knew me.

Born To Try

Words & Music by Delta Goodrem & Audius Mtawanra

Predictable

Words & Music by Delta Goodrem, Kara Dioguardi & Jarred Rodgers

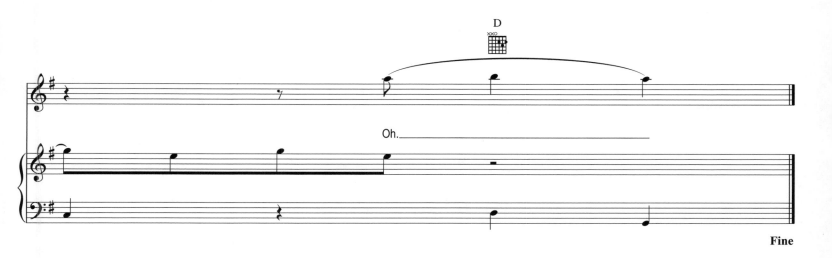

Oh._____

Fine

(Additional lyrics)

Verse 2
I run,
You say you won't give up the chase.
You say you'll follow me any place,
So you can make the same mistakes.
You know just what to do,
And how to use, the best of you,
To try and change my mind.
My eyes are opening this time,
And I read you.

Will You Fall For Me

Words & Music by Delta Goodrem

Original key B Major

Lyrics:

Oh___ oh, hey._____ My

1. head's full of thoughts,___ thoughts of you.__ And I'm dis-trac-ted so ea___sy,
2. (See additional lyrics)
3.

think-ing what to do.___ So un___ sure,___ so un-fa-mi-li-ar.___ Am I

wrong,___ do you think, that some-thing could hap-pen?___ Will you fall___ for me,___

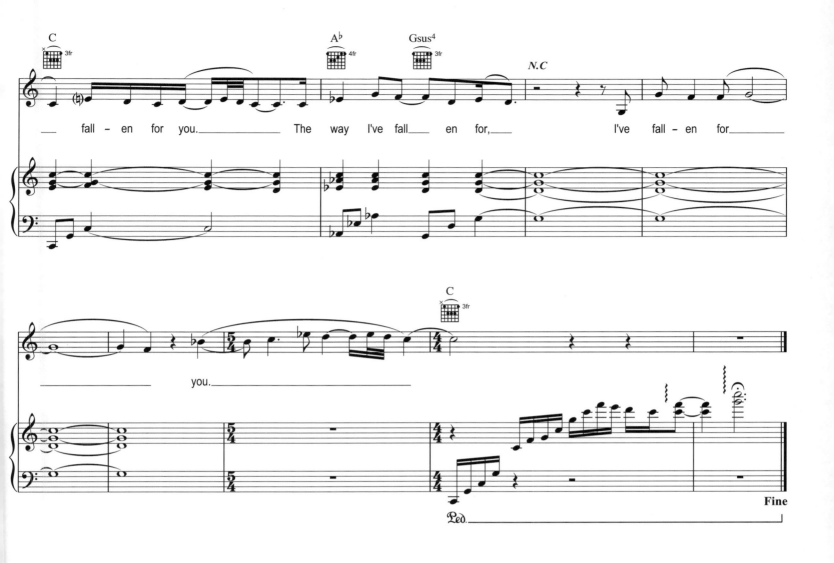

(Additional lyrics)

Verse 2

I'm not acting like myself,
And I'm playing the role of someone else.
And my hearts beating so fast,
I can't stop it.
And I'm so unsure, so unfamiliar,
Am I wrong, do you think, that something could happen?

Verse 3

So unsure, so unfamiliar,
Am I wrong, do you think, that something could happen?
Was I wrong to think I...

Lost Without You

Words & Music by Bridget Benenate & Matthew Gerrard

1. I know I can be a lit-tle stub-born some-times   and I'd say
2. How'm I ev-er gon-na get   rid   of   these   blues?

1/04 (49903)